PERCENTS

GLOBE FEARON EDUCATIONAL PUBLISHER
A Division of Simon & Schuster
Upper Saddle River, New Jersey

Executive Editor: Barbara Levadi
Editors: Bernice Golden, Lynn Kloss, Bob McIlwaine, Kirsten Richert, Tom Repensek
Production Manager: Penny Gibson
Production Editor: Walt Niedner
Interior Design: The Wheetley Company
Electronic Page Production: The Wheetley Company
Cover Design: Pat Smythe

Reviewers:

Lorraine Carlozzi
Assistant Principal for Mathematics
Midwood High School, Brooklyn, NY

Cheryl Miller
Mathematics Teacher
Forestville High School, Forestville, MD

Printed in the United States of America 2 3 4 5 6 7 8 9 10 99 98

ISBN 0-8359-1553-0

GLOBE FEARON EDUCATIONAL PUBLISHER
A Division of Simon & Schuster
Upper Saddle River, New Jersey

CONTENTS

TO THE STUDENT

Access to Math is a series of 15 books designed to help you learn new skills and practice these skills in mathematics. You'll learn the steps necessary to solve a range of mathematical problems.

LESSONS HAVE THE FOLLOWING FEATURES:

❖ Lessons are easy to use. Many begin with a sample problem from a real-life experience. After the sample problem is introduced, you are taught step-by-step how to find the answer. Examples show you how to use your skills.

❖ The *Guided Practice* section demonstrates how to solve a problem similar to the sample problem. Answers are given in the first part of the problem to help you find the final answer.

❖ The *Exercises* section gives you the opportunity to practice the skill presented in the lesson.

❖ The *Application* section applies the math skill in a practical or real-life situation. You will learn how to put your knowledge into action by using manipulatives and calculators, and by working problems through with a partner or a group.

Each book ends with *Cumulative Reviews*. These reviews will help you determine if you have learned the skills in the previous lessons. The *Selected Answers* section at the end of each book lists answers to the odd-numbered exercises. Use the answers to check your work.

Working carefully through the exercises in this book will help you understand and appreciate math in your daily life. You'll also gain more confidence in your math skills.

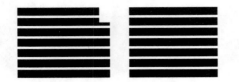

THE MEANING OF PERCENT

Vocabulary

percent: a given part compared to one hundred parts

The % sign stands for percent. But what does the word percent mean? One definition of the word percent is a given part compared to one hundred parts. Read the examples below.

Each grid has 100 squares. What percent of each grid is shaded?

25 squares are shaded.
25 squares compared to
  100 squares are shaded.
25% of the grid is shaded.

7 squares are shaded.
7 squares compared to
  100 squares are shaded.
7% of the grid is shaded.

Guided Practice

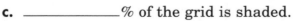

1. What percent of the grid is shaded?

   a. The grid has _____*100*_____ squares.

   b. How many squares are

      shaded? _____

   c. _____% of the grid is shaded.

2. What percent of the grid is shaded?

   a. The grid has _____ squares.

   b. How many squares are

      shaded? _____

   c. _____% of the grid is shaded.

2 PERCENTS

Exercises

Write the percent for the shaded part.

3.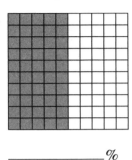

_____%

4.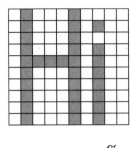

_____%

5.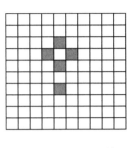

_____%

Shade each grid to show the given percent.

6. 34%

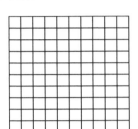

7. 83%

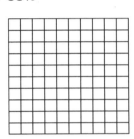

8. 1%

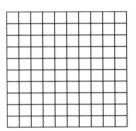

Application

Answer the following questions.

9. There are 100 pennies in a dollar. If Juan has 50% of a dollar, how many pennies does he have?

_____

10. Jasmin answered 85 questions out of 100. What percent of the questions did she answer?

_____

11. One hundred runners started in the McAllen, Texas, Marathon. You decide how many runners finished the race. Write a sentence about the percent of runners that finished.

_____

_____

_____

PERCENTS AND DECIMALS

Vocabulary

decimal: a number with one or more digits to the right of the decimal point.

A given part compared to one hundred parts can be written as a percent or as a decimal.

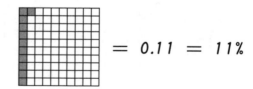

$= 0.11 = 11\%$

Many states tax the money workers earn. This tax is called income tax. In some states, the income tax is 11 cents on every dollar, or 11 cents out of every 100 cents. What percent is the income tax in those states?

11 cents out of 100 cents can be written as a decimal or as a percent.

$$11 \text{ cents} = 0.11 = 11\%$$

The income tax in those states is 11%.

To change *a decimal to a percent,* move the decimal point two places to the right and write the percent sign.

$$0.11 = .11 = 11\%$$

Sometimes a decimal number has more than two places.

$$0.234 = 0.234 = 23.4\%$$

If the decimal number has only one place to the right of the decimal point, write a zero to the right of the decimal numeral.

$$0.9 = 0.90 = 90\%$$

To change *a percent to a decimal,* remove the percent sign and move the decimal point two places to the left.

$$21\% = 21. = 0.21 \qquad 2\% = 02. = 0.02$$

Guided Practice

1. Write 0.37 as a percent.

    a. Move the decimal point two places to the right.

         0.37 _____

    b. Write 0.37 as a percent. _____

2. Write 75% as a decimal.

    a. Remove the percent sign. _____

    b. Move the decimal point two places to the left.

    _____

    c. Write 75% as a decimal. _____

Exercises

Write each decimal as a percent.

3. 0.20

_____

4. 0.08

_____

5. 0.155

_____

6. 0.7

_____

7. 0.55

_____

8. 0.4

_____

Write each percent as a decimal.

9. 50%

_____

10. 6%

_____

11. 97%

_____

12. 18%

_____

13. 1%

_____

14. 33%

_____

Write each amount as a decimal and as a percent of a dollar.

15. Fifteen cents

_____, _____%

16. A quarter

_____, _____%

17. Ninety cents

_____, _____%

Application

COOPERATIVE LEARNING

Work with a partner to answer these questions.

18. Many states put a sales tax on items you purchase. The sales tax amount is added to each purchase, and this amount is paid to the state.

    a. A sales tax may be $.06 on every dollar spent. A tax of $.06 is a _____% tax.

    b. If a state has a 5% sales tax, how much will be added to a $1.00 purchase for the tax? _____

PERCENTS AND FRACTIONS

fraction: a number that names a part of a whole

$$\frac{1}{4} \quad \begin{matrix} \leftarrow \text{numerator} \\ \leftarrow \text{denominator} \end{matrix}$$

Reminder

To change a fraction to a decimal, divide the numerator of the fraction by the denominator.

In his social studies book, Kevin reads, "About one-fourth of the world's population lives in China."

Kerry reads, "Approximately 25 percent of the world's population lives in China."

Gina says, "The fraction, one-fourth, and 25 percent mean the same thing."

To compare $\frac{1}{4}$ to 25%, you can write $\frac{1}{4}$ as a percent. Or you can write 25% as a fraction.

To change *a fraction to a percent,* first change the fraction to a decimal. Then, change the decimal to a percent.

$$\text{fraction} \longrightarrow \text{decimal} \qquad \text{decimal} \longrightarrow \text{percent}$$

$$\frac{1}{4} = 4\overline{)1.00}^{\,0.25} \qquad\qquad 0.25 = 25\%$$

So, $\frac{1}{4}$ equals 25%. Gina was correct.

Sometimes when you change a fraction to a decimal, you have a remainder.

$$\text{fraction} \longrightarrow \text{decimal} \qquad \text{decimal} \longrightarrow \text{percent}$$

$$\frac{1}{3} = 3\overline{)1.00}^{\,33\frac{1}{3}} \qquad 33\tfrac{1}{3} = 33\tfrac{1}{3}\%$$
$$\begin{array}{r} 9 \\ \hline 10 \\ 9 \\ \hline 1 \end{array}$$

To change *a percent to a fraction,* first remove the percent sign. Next, write the percent as a fraction with a denominator of 100. Then write the fraction in simplest form.

$$\begin{array}{c} \text{fraction with a} \\ \text{denominator of 100} \end{array} \qquad\qquad \text{simplest form}$$

$$25\% = \frac{25}{100} \qquad\qquad \frac{25}{100} \overset{\div 25}{\underset{\div 25}{=}} \frac{1}{4}$$

So, 25% equals $\frac{1}{4}$.

Guided Practice

1. Write $\frac{3}{4}$ as a percent.

    a. Write $\frac{3}{4}$ as a decimal. $\frac{3}{4} =$ _____0.75_____

    b. Write the decimal as a percent. _____

2. Write 10% as a fraction.

    a. Remove the percent sign. Write the percent as a fraction with a denominator of 100. _____

    b. Write the fraction in simplest form. _____

Exercises

Write each fraction as a percent.

3. $\frac{1}{5}$

4. $\frac{3}{10}$

5. $\frac{3}{8}$

_____   _____   _____

Write each percent as a fraction in simplest form.

6. 50%

7. 4%

8. 60%

_____   _____   _____

Application

9. You can use mental math to write a percent for a fraction with a denominator that is a factor of 100. (Factor of 100 means the denominator divides into 100 evenly.) Find a mental shortcut to write these fractions as percents.

$\frac{1}{2} =$ _____ % $\frac{32}{100} =$ _____ % $\frac{2}{5} =$ _____ %

$\frac{6}{10} =$ _____ % $\frac{4}{5} =$ _____ % $\frac{1}{20} =$ _____ %

10. Describe your mental math shortcut.

    _____

    _____

    _____

PERCENTS GREATER THAN 100%

Vocabulary

mixed number: a number made up of a whole number and a fraction

A percent can be greater than 100%. This means there is more than one whole.

The grid has 100 squares.

100 squares are shaded.

$\frac{100}{100} = 1$ whole, or 100% is shaded.

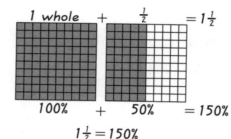

1 grid and $\frac{1}{2}$ of another are shaded. 150 squares are shaded.

$\frac{100}{100} + \frac{50}{100} = \frac{150}{100}$. This means 150% is shaded.

To change *a **mixed number*** *to a percent*, first change the mixed number to a fraction. Change the fraction to a decimal.

$$\text{mixed number} \longrightarrow \text{fraction}$$
$$2\frac{1}{2} = \frac{5}{2}$$

$$\text{fraction} \longrightarrow \text{decimal}$$
$$\frac{5}{2} = 2\overline{)5.0}^{\,2.5}$$

Then change the decimal to a percent.

$$\text{decimal} \longrightarrow \text{percent}$$
$$2.50 = 250\%$$

To change *a percent to a mixed number*, first remove the percent sign. Next, write the percent as a fraction with a denominator of 100. Then write the fraction in simplest form. Change the fraction to a mixed number.

$$\text{fraction with a denominator of 100}$$
$$250\% = \frac{250}{100}$$

$$\text{simplest form}$$
$$\frac{250}{100} \overset{\div 50}{\underset{\div 50}{=}} \frac{5}{2} = 2\frac{1}{2}$$

1. Write $1\frac{1}{5}$ as a percent.

    a. Write $1\frac{1}{5}$ as a fraction. _____ $\frac{6}{5}$ _____

    b. Write the fraction as a decimal. _____ *1.2* _____

    c. Write the decimal as a percent. _____

2. Write 125% as a mixed number.

    a. Write 125% as a fraction with a denominator of 100. _____

    b. Write the fraction in simplest form. _____

Exercises

Write each mixed number as a percent.

3. $1\frac{3}{4}$

4. $2\frac{3}{5}$

5. $2\frac{1}{4}$

_____   _____   _____

6. $1\frac{4}{8}$

7. $3\frac{3}{10}$

8. $3\frac{4}{5}$

_____   _____   _____

Write each percent as a mixed number.

9. 175%

10. 350%

11. 225%

_____   _____   _____

12. 275%

13. 375%

14. 425%

_____   _____   _____

Application

15. Shanti and Deb started a T-shirt decorating business. At first, they estimated that they would get 4 T-shirt orders a month. However, they got 125% of this estimate in the first month. Did they get more or fewer orders than they'd planned? Explain your answer.

_____

_____

Vocabulary

equivalent: having the same value

FINDING EQUIVALENT FRACTIONS, DECIMALS, AND PERCENTS

A number less than one can be written as a percent, a decimal, or a fraction.

Example 1

The circle graph at the right shows that about 70% of the earth's surface is water.

The bar graph at the right shows the same fact. You can say that 0.7 of the earth's surface is water.

This pie chart shows this fact. You can see that $\frac{7}{10}$ of the earth's surface is water.

In these examples the percent, decimal, and fraction values are all the same. They are **equivalent.**

$$70\% = 0.7 = \frac{7}{10}$$

Reminder

Percent means *per hundred.*

To write 70% as a decimal, think of 70% as 70 hundredths. Move the decimal point two places to the left and drop the percent sign.

$$70\% = 0.70 \text{ or } 0.7$$

To write 70% as a fraction, think of 70% as 70 hundredths. Write a fraction with 70 over a denominator of 100. Then write the fraction in simplest form.

$$70\% = \frac{70}{100} = \frac{7}{10} \text{ simplest form}$$

Other examples:

$$25\% = 0.25 \qquad 25\% = \frac{25}{100} = \frac{1}{4}$$

So, 25%, 0.25, and $\frac{1}{4}$ are equivalent.

$$50\% = 0.5 \qquad 50\% = \frac{50}{100} = \frac{1}{2}$$

So, 50%, 0.5, and $\frac{1}{2}$ are equivalent.

Example 2

The grid at the right represents the substances that make up the human body. About $\frac{3}{5}$ of the human body is water.

You can divide the grid to show that $\frac{3}{5}$ is the same as 0.6.

This grid shows that 0.6 is the same as 60%. About 60% of the human body is water.

As demonstrated above, the same amount can be represented in three equivalent forms:

$$\frac{3}{5} = 0.6 = 60\%$$

To write a decimal as a percent, move the decimal point two places to the right and write the percent sign.

$$0.60 = 60\%$$

Reminder

Remember, $\frac{3}{5}$ means $3 \div 5$.

To write a fraction as a percent, change the fraction to a decimal. Then write the decimal as a percent.

$$\frac{3}{5} = 3 \div 5 = 0.60 = 60\%$$

Other examples:

$$\frac{3}{4} = 3 \div 4 = 0.75 = 75\%$$

$$\frac{1}{8} = 1 \div 8 = 0.125 = 12.5\%$$

Guided Practice

1. Write 40% as a decimal.

   a. Remove the percent sign. _____ 40. _____

   b. Move the decimal point two places to the left.

   _____ 40. _____

   c. What decimal is equivalent to 40%?

   _____

2. Write 35% as a fraction.

    a. 35% means 35 out of _____ or $\frac{35}{100}$.

    b. Write the fraction in simplest form. $\frac{35}{100}$ =

    _____

3. Write 0.375 as a percent.

    a. Move the decimal point two places to the right.

    _____

    b. Write the percent sign. _____

4. Write $\frac{7}{8}$ as a percent.

    a. $\frac{7}{8}$ means _____ ÷ _____.

    b. $\frac{7}{8}$ written as a decimal is _____.

    c. Change the decimal to a percent. _____

Exercises

Complete.

5. Write the fraction. _____

6. Write the decimal. _____

7. Write the percent. _____

Draw a line to match the percent with the equivalent fraction or decimal.

8. 10%	**a.** 0.32
9. 20%	**b.** $\frac{4}{25}$
10. 85%	**c.** 0.1
11. 16%	**d.** $\frac{5}{8}$
12. $66\frac{2}{3}\%$	**e.** $\frac{1}{5}$
13. 32%	**f.** 0.8
14. 80%	**g.** $\frac{2}{3}$
15. 62.5%	**h.** 0.85

Complete the table. The first row has been done for you.

Fraction	Decimal	Percent
$\frac{1}{5}$	0.2	20%
$\frac{1}{10}$	16. _____	17. _____
18. _____	0.25	19. _____
20. _____	21. _____	40%
22. _____	0.75	23. _____
$\frac{5}{6}$	24. _____	25. _____
26. _____	27. _____	50%
$\frac{4}{5}$	28. _____	29. _____
30. _____	31. _____	100%

32. • On a piece of graph paper draw a line around a grid 10 × 10 square. Cut out the square.

   • Fold the square in half to form a rectangle.

   • Fold the rectangle in half to form a small square.

   • Unfold the piece of paper.

   a. How many small squares did you make? _____

   b. One small square is what fraction of the large square? _____

   c. How many grid squares are in one small square? _____

   d. How would you write that number as a decimal amount of the large square? _____

   e. What percent of the large square is one small square? _____

FINDING THE PERCENT OF A NUMBER, EQUATION METHOD

Vocabulary

equation: a number sentence with equal sign (=)

A survey of 250 students shows that 30% choose pizza as their favorite food and 20% choose hamburgers. How many students choose pizza?

Reminder

The word *of* means multiply.

The amount you need to find is 30% of 250 students. The 30% is called the rate, or the percent. The 250 students is the base, or the total number of students.

Now set up an **equation** to find the amount. You can change the percent to a decimal.

$$Amount \ = \ rate \ \times \ base$$

$$What \ is \ 30\% \ of \ 250?$$

$$a \ = \ 0.30 \ \times \ 250$$

$$a \ = \ 75$$

Out of 250 students, 75 choose pizza.

You can also change the percent to a fraction to find the percent of a number. How many students choose hamburgers as their favorite food?

$$Amount \ = \ rate \ \times \ base$$

$$What \ is \ 20\% \ of \ 250?$$

$$a \ = \ \frac{20}{100} \ \times \ 250$$

$$a \ = \ \frac{1}{5} \ \times \ 250$$

$$a \ = \ 50$$

Out of 250 students, 50 choose hamburgers.

Guided Practice

1. In a survey of 240 high school students, 65% say they like math. How many students say they like math?

   a. What is the total number of students? _240_

   b. What percent of the students like math? _65%_

   c. What is the base? _240_

   d. What is the rate? _65%_

   e. Write an equation to solve the problem. Use a decimal for the percent.

   $a =$ _0.65_ $\times$ _240_

   $a =$ _____

Exercises

Write an equation using fractions or decimals to find each number.

2. 50% of 100 = _____

3. 10% of 300 = _____

4. 25% of 200 = _____

5. 100% of 153 = _____

6. 90% of 360 = _____

7. 8% of 125 = _____

8. 20% of 24 = _____

9. 15% of 320 = _____

10. $33\frac{1}{3}$% of 60 = _____

Application

 Solve the following percent problems. Do them mentally, use a calculator, or use pencil and paper, whichever is faster for you.

11. 10% of 200 = _____

12. 50% of 120 = _____

13. 35% of 80 = _____

14. 85% of 240 = _____

15. 25% of 16 = _____

16. 22% of 550 = _____

17. Explain why some calculations can be done faster without a calculator.

_____

_____

_____

FINDING THE PERCENT OF A NUMBER, PROPORTION METHOD

Vocabulary

ratio: a comparison of two numbers, sometimes expressed as a fraction

proportion: a statement that two ratios are equal

Soccer is the most popular sport in Colombia. One season, Tonio scored 25% of the shots that he attempted in the 12 games that he played. If Tonio attempted 36 shots, how many goals did he score?

To solve this problem, we can use a proportion. A **proportion** is a statement showing that two **ratios**, or number comparisons, are equal.

$$\frac{\text{rate}}{100} = \frac{\text{number of goals}}{\text{base}}$$

Reminder

The base is the total. The rate is the percent.

Write the rate, 25%, as 25. You know the base, the total number of shots Tonio attempted, 36. Let g stand for the number of goals Tonio scored.

$$\frac{25}{100} = \frac{g}{36} \qquad \text{Write a proportion.}$$

$$100 \times g = 25 \times 36 \qquad \text{Cross multiply.}$$

$$100g = 900$$

Reminder

Cross products in a proportion are equal.

$$\frac{100g}{100} = \frac{900}{100} \qquad \text{Divide both sides of the equation by 100.}$$

$$g = 9 \qquad \text{Solve for } g.$$

Tonio scored 9 goals.

Guided Practice

1. There are 15 players on Gino's team and 20% of them favor their left foot. How many players favor their left foot?

   a. Write a proportion. $\frac{20}{100} = \frac{n}{15}$

   b. Cross multiply. $100n = \underline{300}$

   c. Divide both sides by 100. $\frac{100n}{100} = \underline{\hspace{2cm}}$

   d. Solve for n. $n = \underline{\hspace{2cm}}$

Exercises

 Write and solve a proportion to find each amount. You may use your calculator to help you multiply.

2. What is 42% of 850? _____

3. 95% of 310 is what number? _____

4. What is 25% of 420? _____

5. 30% of 70 is what number? _____

6. 62% of 250 is what number? _____

7. What is 55% of 620? _____

8. What is 12.5% of 424? _____

9. 36% of 132 is what number? _____

Application

10. Find 28% of 245.

    a. Use both the equation method and the proportion method to find the answer.

    _____

    b. Discuss which method you prefer and why.

    _____

    _____

DISCOUNT

Vocabulary

discount rate: the percentage of the original price an item is reduced

discount: the dollar amount by which the original price of an item is reduced

list price: the original price of an item

sale price: the price the consumer will pay after the discount has been subtracted from the list price

Reminder

To change a percent to a decimal, move the decimal two places to the left and remove the percent sign.

Tyrone is looking for a good buy on a portable CD player. He sees an advertisement in a local paper and decides to buy the CD player. How much is he going to pay?

First, Tyrone needs to find the **discount,** or the dollar amount he will save. The **discount rate** is 15% of the **list price**.

> **The Daily Herald**
> - - - - - - - - -
> Get a CD Player! Mention this ad and get **15% off** of a **$180** value. Visit Sam's CDs today!

Discount	=	Rate	×	List price
↓		↓		↓
	=	15%	×	$180
	=	0.15	×	$180
	=	$27		

The discount on the portable CD player is $27.

Now that Tyrone knows the amount of the discount, he can calculate the **sale price**—the discount subtracted from the list price.

Sale price	=	List price	−	Discount
↓		↓		↓
	=	$180	−	$27
	=	$153		

Tyrone will pay $153 for the CD player.

Guided Practice

1. How much would a set of $120 speakers cost with a 25% discount?

   a. Write the rate as a decimal. _0.25_

   b. What is the list price? _$120_

   c. Find the discount amount.

   _____ × _____ = _____

   d. Find the sale price.

   _____ × _____ = _____

Exercises

Find the sale price. You may wish to use a calculator to help you multiply. Round your answers to the nearest cent.

2. $150 with a 20% discount

   Sale price = _____

3. $10 with a 5% discount

   Sale price = _____

4. $1,100 with a 30% discount

   Sale price = _____

5. $24.92 with a 10% discount

   Sale price = _____

6. $85 with a 40% discount

   Sale price = _____

7. $24.99 with a 30% discount

   Sale price = _____

Application

8. A portable CD player that sells for $299 has a discount of 15%. Jasmine calculated the sale price for the portable CD player by finding 85% of $299. Why does Jasmine's method work?

   _____

   _____

   _____

9. Use Jasmine's method to find the sale price of a $115 coat with a 30% discount.

   _____

SALES TAX

Vocabulary

sales tax rate: a percentage of the cost of a purchased item

sales tax: the dollar amount that is added to the item price at the time of sale

In most states, when you purchase an item, you must pay a **sales tax**. This amount is added on to the price of the item. The tax that is collected goes to the local and state governments. Different cities and states have different **sales tax rates**.

Gina buys a new pair of basketball sneakers. There is a 7.5% sales tax rate in her town. How much does she pay for the sneakers?

To find the sales tax, multiply the cost of the sneakers by the sales tax rate.

$$\text{Sales tax} = \text{Cost} \times \text{Sales tax rate}$$
$$= \$125.50 \times 7.5\%$$
$$= \$125.50 \times 0.075$$
$$= \$9.4125$$

The sales tax to the nearest cent is $9.41.

To find how much Gina will pay for the sneakers, add the tax to the cost of the sneakers.

$$\text{Purchase price} = \text{Cost} + \text{Tax}$$
$$= \$125.50 + \$9.41$$
$$= \$134.91$$

Gina pays $134.91 for the sneakers.

Guided Practice

1. Jade wants to buy a basketball for $65.90. The tax rate is 5%. What is the total amount Jade will pay?

   a. Write the sales tax rate as a decimal. _0.05_

   b. What is the price of the basketball? _$65.90_

Reminder

When working with money amounts, round to the nearest cent.

c. Find the sales tax.

_____ × _____ = _____

d. Find the total purchase price.

_____ + _____ = _____

Exercises

 Your team wants to purchase the following items. Find the sales tax and total purchase price for each item. You may use a calculator to help you multiply.

2. Backboard set: $620, 4% tax

Sales tax: _____

Purchase price: _____

3. Warm-up suit: $130.80, 5% tax

Sales tax: _____

Purchase price: _____

4. Game uniform: $65.50, 8% tax

Sales tax: _____

Purchase price: _____

5. Scoreboard: $1,280, 5.5% tax

Sales tax: _____

Purchase price: _____

6. Set of balls: $139.60, 7% tax

Sales tax: _____

Purchase price: _____

7. Practice uniform: $18.90, 4.5% tax

Sales tax: _____

Purchase price: _____

Application

 COOPERATIVE LEARNING

Work with a partner to solve each problem.

8. To coach a neighborhood basketball team, you purchase the following items: stopwatch, $19.99; clipboard, $13.29; whistle, $2.95. Create an efficient way to find the purchase price if the sales tax rate is 6%.

_____

9. Mario saw a jacket on sale for $78. The sales tax rate was 5%. Mario used a shortcut to calculate the purchase price. He multiplied the cost of the jacket by 105%. Explain what he did and what the purchase price was.

_____

_____

SIMPLE INTEREST

Vocabulary

interest: the amount of money paid to a lender or a saver

interest rate: the percentage of the principal charged as interest

principal: the amount of money borrowed or saved

time: the length of time in years the principal is loaned or saved

Am Iye had to borrow $3,500 to purchase a sports car. The amount he borrowed is called the **principal**. Am Iye must pay to borrow the money for four years (the length of **time**). This payment is called **interest**. The **interest rate** is a percent of the principal. Simple interest is calculated by using a formula.

Example 1

Am Iye's interest rate is 6%. How much interest will he pay for the four years?

Substitute the numbers in the formula.

$$
\begin{array}{ccccccc}
\text{Interest} & = & \text{principal} & \times & \text{rate} & \times & \text{time} \\
I & = & p & \times & r & \times & t \\
& & \downarrow & & \downarrow & & \downarrow \\
& = & \$3{,}500 & \times & 0.06 & \times & 4 \\
& = & \$840 & & & &
\end{array}
$$

Am Iye will pay $840 interest for borrowing the money.

Example 2

Chan invested $550 at 3% for 9 months. How much interest did he earn?

9 months $= \frac{9}{12} = \frac{3}{4}$ year, or 0.75

$$
\begin{array}{ccccccc}
\text{Interest} & = & \text{principal} & \times & \text{rate} & \times & \text{time} \\
I & = & p & \times & r & \times & t \\
& & \downarrow & & \downarrow & & \downarrow \\
& = & \$550 & \times & 0.03 & \times & 0.75 \\
& = & \$12.375 & & & &
\end{array}
$$

We must round $12.375 to the nearest cent. Chan earned $12.38 interest on his investment.

Reminder

Write the rate as a decimal.

Reminder

If you borrow money, you pay interest. If you deposit or invest money, you often earn interest.

Reminder

Time is measured in years. Write months as fractions of a year.

Guided Practice

1. Sarita opened a savings account with $750. If the bank pays simple interest at a rate of 3.5% per year, how much will Sarita earn after 3 years?

   a. What is the simple interest formula?

   $I = \underline{p} \times \underline{r} \times \underline{t}$

   b. Substitute the principal, the rate, and the time into the formula. Use a decimal for the rate.

   $I = \underline{\$750} \times \underline{0.035} \times \underline{3}$

   c. How much interest will Sarita earn after 3 years? _____

Exercises

 Calculate the interest. You may use a calculator to help you multiply. The first one is started for you.

2. $100 at 5% for 1 year

   $I = 100 \times 0.05 \times 1$

   $I = $ _____

3. $300 at 4.5% for 2 years

   $I = $ _____

4. $380 at 12% for 2.5 years

   $I = $ _____

5. $700 at 18% for 6 months

   $I = $ _____

Application

COOPERATIVE LEARNING

Complete the following problem with a partner.

6. When you use a credit card, you borrow money. Credit cards often have high rates of interest. Suppose you and your partner have an $1,800 credit card bill.

   a. How much interest would you pay at 17% for one month?

   (Hint: Use $\frac{1}{12}$ for the time.) _____

   b. Discuss some pros and cons of using credit cards.

   _____

   _____

   _____

ESTIMATING WITH PERCENTS

Vocabulary

estimate: to determine a number close to an exact amount

Music-for-Less is offering a 23% discount on a CD player that normally sells for $129.95. Sam has $100. He **estimates** the amount of the discount to see if he can buy the CD player.

Sam uses compatible numbers to estimate 23% of $129.95.

$$23\% \dashrightarrow 25\% = \frac{1}{4}$$

$$\$129.95 \dashrightarrow \$128$$

$$\$128 \div 4 = \$32$$

$\frac{1}{4}$ of $128 = $32.

Sam's discount is about $32. So, he can buy the CD player with $100.

When estimating with percents, round the percent to an everyday percent and use its equivalent fraction.

$$10\% = \frac{1}{10} \qquad 20\% = \frac{1}{5} \qquad 33\frac{1}{3}\% = \frac{1}{3}$$

$$25\% = \frac{1}{4} \qquad 50\% = \frac{1}{2} \qquad 75\% = \frac{3}{4}$$

To find a percent of a number, divide the number by the denominator of the fraction when the numerator is 1. For example, to find 20% of a number, divide the number by 5.

Guided Practice

1. Estimate 19.6% of 139.

   a. Round 19.6%. <u>20%</u>

   b. Write the percent as a fraction. $\frac{1}{5}$

   c. Round 139. _____

   d. Divide. _____ ÷ _____ = _____

2. Estimate 77% of 188.

    a. Write 77% as an everyday percent. _____

    b. Write the percent as a fraction. _____

    c. Write 188 as a compatible number for the fraction.

    _____

    d. The estimate is _____ .

Exercises

Estimate each answer.

3. 33% of 600

_____

4. 45.7% of 250

_____

5. 10% of 92

_____

6. 20% of 58

_____

7. 73% of 363

_____

8. 26% of 111

_____

9. 16.8% of 489

_____

10. $8\frac{1}{2}$% of 63

_____

Application

11. Concha bought a jacket for $84.95. Estimate the sales tax she will pay if the sales tax rate is $7\frac{3}{4}$%.

_____

_____

12. Explain why Concha should estimate the amount of the sales tax before the clerk rings up her purchase on the register.

_____

_____

PERCENTS BETWEEN 0% AND 1%

Lida works at a concession stand. Today, her boss said, "Good news! This month's sales were 0.5% better than last month's." Lida asked, "What does 0.5% mean?" Her boss said, "0.5% means one half of one percent. It is less than 1%. But it is greater than zero."

1% is one hundredth, or one part out of 100

0.5% is one half of one hundredth, or one half of one part out of 100

Some percents, like 0.5%, are between 0% and 1%. Working with these percents is just like working with any other percent.

To change a *percent to a decimal*, remove the percent sign and move the decimal point two places to the left.

$$0.5\% = 0.005 \qquad 0.18\% = 0.0018$$

To change a *decimal to a percent*, move the decimal point two places to the right and write the percent sign.

$$0.0073 = 0.73\% \qquad 0.002 = 0.2\%$$

To change a *percent to a fraction*, remove the percent sign. Change the percent to a decimal and write the decimal as a fraction. Then write the fraction in simplest form.

$$0.4\% = 0.004 = \frac{4}{1,000} = \frac{1}{250}$$

To change a *fraction to a percent*, write the fraction as a decimal. Then change the decimal to a percent.

$$\frac{3}{400} = 3 \div 400 = 0.0075 = 0.75\%$$

1. Write 0.3% as a decimal.

   a. Remove the percent sign. <u>0.3</u>

   b. Move the decimal point two places to the left.
   <u>000.3</u>

2. Write 0.62% as a fraction.

   a. Remove the percent sign. Change the percent to a decimal. _____

   b. Write the decimal as a fraction. _____

   c. Write the fraction in simplest form.
   _____

Reminder

0.0062 is $\frac{62}{10,000}$

Exercises

Complete the table.

Fraction	Decimal	Percent
$\frac{1}{125}$	**3.**	0.8%
4.	0.007	**5.**
$\frac{1}{800}$	**6.**	**7.**
8.	**9.**	0.875%

Application

10. Cosmo's Records reported a 0.25% increase in monthly sales in July. The same month, Second Hand Tunes reported a 2.5% increase in monthly sales.

    a. Which store had the greater increase? _____

    b. Explain how you arrived at your answer. Draw a diagram if that will help with your explanation.

    _____

    _____

    _____

 # FINDING THE RATE, EQUATION METHOD

Mrs. Torres will make a taco dinner for the family. Out of the family's $125 weekly budget for groceries, she has spent $22 on ground beef, chicken, taco shells, lettuce, cheese, and salsa. What percent of the grocery budget did Mrs. Torres spend?

To find what percent of $125 is $22, you can use a formula.

Reminder

The rate, *r*, is the percent. The base is the total. The amount is the part of the total that you are given or want to find.

$$\text{Rate} \times \text{Base} = \text{Amount}$$

$$r \times \$125 = \$22$$

$r \times \$125$	$=$	$\$22$	Write the equation.
$r \times \dfrac{125}{125}$	$=$	$\dfrac{22}{125}$	Divide both sides by 125.
r	$=$	$\dfrac{22}{125}$	Solve the equation for *r*.
r	$=$	0.176	
r	$=$	17.6%	Change the decimal to a percent.

Reminder

To change a decimal to a percent, move the decimal point two places to the right and write the percent symbol.

Rounding to the nearest whole percent, Mrs. Torres spent 18% of the grocery budget.

Guided Practice

1. What percent of 48 is 24?

   a. Write an equation.
   $r \times 48 = \underline{\ 24\ }$

Reminder

You can use the division symbol or write a fraction to show division.
$4 \div 2$ or $\dfrac{4}{2}$

   b. Solve the equation for *r*.
   $r \times \underline{\ 48\ } \div \underline{\ 48\ } = \underline{\ 24\ } \div \underline{\ 48\ }$

   $r = \underline{\hspace{2cm}}$

   c. Change the decimal to a percent.

   $r = \underline{\hspace{2cm}}$

Write and solve an equation to find the rate. Round your answer to the nearest whole percent.

2. What percent of 5 is 3?

_____

3. What percent of 12 is 9?

_____

4. What percent of 20 is 7?

_____

5. What percent of 120 is 15?

_____

6. What percent of 150 is 11?

_____

7. What percent of 800 is 250?

_____

8. The Gallo's have a $135 food budget for Jennifer's birthday party. Mr. Gallo spent $17.28 on beverages. What percent of the food budget did he spend?

_____

9. Taran received tips from 26 of the 28 tables he waited on. What percent of his tables gave Taran a tip?

_____

Application

10. You can use mental math to find rates. Use this formula to find rates mentally.

$$\text{Rate} = \frac{\text{Amount}}{\text{Base}}$$

a. What percent of 2 is 1?

_____

b. What percent of 36 is 9?

_____

c. What percent of 25 is 5?

_____

d. What percent of 10 is 10?

_____

e. Explain why the shortcut works.

_____

_____

_____

 # FINDING THE RATE, PROPORTION METHOD

Leroy Jackson took a state test of skills in mathematics, language, map reading, and the use of reference materials. The table below shows his raw scores—the total number of items on each subtest and the number Leroy answered correctly on each subtest. How did Leroy do on the Reading subtest?

Reminder

A proportion is a statement that two ratios are equal. Cross products in a proportion are equal.

Subtest	Correct Items	Total Number of Items
Reading	12	15
Language Usage	12	20
Spelling	10	16
Math Computation	10	14
Math Skills	9	10
Math Reasoning	6	9
Map Skills	7	8
Reference Materials	6	8
Total	**72**	**100**

To find the percent of the total Leroy answered correctly, you can use the proportion method.

$$\frac{\text{Rate}}{100} = \frac{\text{Number Correct}}{\text{Total}}$$

Reminder

Since percent means parts per 100, think of "what percent" as $\frac{r}{100}$.

On the Reading subtest, what percent of 15 is 12?

$$\frac{r}{100} = \frac{12}{15} \qquad \text{Write a proportion.}$$

$$15 \times r = 100 \times 12 \qquad \text{Cross multiply.}$$

$$15r = 1,200$$

$$r = 80 \qquad \text{Divide both sides by 15.}$$

$$\frac{80}{100} = 80\% \qquad \text{Write the percent.}$$

Leroy had 80% of the items correct on the Reading subtest.

Guided Practice

1. On the Language Usage subtest, what percent did Leroy get correct?

   a. Write a proportion. $\frac{r}{100} = \frac{12}{20}$

   b. Solve the proportion. $r =$ _____

   c. Write the percent.   _____

2. On the Spelling subtest, what percent did Leroy get correct?

   a. Write a proportion.   _____

   b. Solve the proportion.   _____

   c. Write the percent.   _____

Exercises

 Use the proportion method to find the rate. You may use a calculator to help you multiply and divide. Round your answer to the nearest whole percent.

3. What percent of 5 is 4?   4. What percent of 25 is 8?

   _____   _____

5. What percent of 75 is 45?   6. What percent of 900 is 168?

   _____   _____

Application

 Use the table on page 30 to find Leroy's score to the nearest whole percent for the remaining subtests and for the entire test.

COOPERATIVE LEARNING

7. Math Computation _____   8. Math Skills _____

9. Math Reasoning _____   10. Map Skills _____

11. Reference Materials _____ 12. Total _____

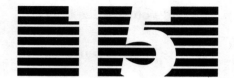

FINDING THE DISCOUNT RATE

Anne was shopping for a prom dress at a discount store. She found the dress shown here.

Original Price: **$100**

Sale Price: **$90**

Reminder

The discount rate is the percentage by which the original price is reduced.

What is the discount rate, or percent off, of this dress?

To figure this out, first Anne found the discount.

Original price − Sale price = Discount

$$\$100 - \$90 = \$10$$

Then she used this formula to find the discount rate.

Rate = Discount ÷ Original price

Reminder

Sometimes it takes more than one step to solve a problem.

$$r = \$10 \div \$100$$

$$r = 0.10, \text{ or } 10\%$$

Anne found a dress she liked that cost 10% less than it would at a regular store.

Guided Practice

Reminder

To change a decimal to a percent, move the decimal point two places to the right and write the percent symbol.

1. Item: CD   Original price: $12   Sale price: $9

   a. Find the discount. $12 − __$9__ = __$3__

   b. Find the discount rate. $r =$ __$3__ ÷ $12

   $r =$ _____ = _____%

2. Item: blue jeans   Original price: $35   Sale price: $28

   a. Find the discount. _____

   b. Find the discount rate. _____

Exercises

 Find the discount and the discount rate on each item. You may use a calculator to help you. Round rates to the nearest whole percent.

3. Item: backpack
Original price: $30
Sale price: $15

_____

4. Item: ceiling fan
Original price: $80
Sale price: $60

_____

5. Item: warm-up suit
Original price: $120
Sale price: $105

_____

6. Item: bicycle
Original price: $175
Sale price: $160

_____

7. Item: binoculars
Original price: $60
Sale price: $50

_____

8. Item: gold chain
Original price: $55
Sale price: $47

_____

Application

9. The list price of a pair of Air-Dunk basketball shoes is $50. Last week, the shoes were on sale for $40. This week, they sell for $30. What is the discount rate each week, compared to the original price?

_____

10. The ads at the right show the same pair of in-line skates at two different stores. At which store can you buy the in-line skates for less? Explain.

Sale **$54**
Original Price **$72**

Roller Fun Skate Store

SALE
16% Off

Original Price $72

✎ _____

_____

_____

FINDING THE SALES TAX RATE

David Fong is preparing a report and a slide show on Chinese New Year celebrations. He buys a book on Chinese culture from a local bookstore. The sales receipt is below.

```
BEST BOOKS
Store 251              2:01 p.m.
5.09147          Chinese Culture
$19.99
Subtotal ............. $19.99
Sales tax ........... $ 1.00
Total ................ $20.99
```

David pays $1.00 more than the price of the book itself. This extra amount is the sales tax. What is the sales tax rate in David's state?

To find the sales tax rate, you can use this formula.

Reminder

The sales tax rate is the percentage of the cost of an item.

Rate = Sales tax ÷ Price

$$r = \$1.00 \div \$19.99$$

$$r = 0.05$$

The sales tax rate is 5%.

Guided Practice

1. Find the sales tax rate for a $10.00 item if the sales tax is $0.60.

   a. Use the formula to write an equation.

   Rate = Sales tax ÷ Price

   r = ___0.60___ ÷ $10.00

   b. Solve the equation. r = _____

   c. Write the percent. _____

2. Find the sales tax rate for a $4.00 item if the sales tax is $0.26.

a. Write an equation.

$r =$ _____ $\div$ _____

b. Solve the equation. $r =$ _____

c. Write the percent. Round to the nearest tenth of a percent. _____

Exercises

 Find the sales tax rate for each item. You can use a calculator to help you divide. Round your answer to the nearest tenth of a percent.

3. Item: calendar
   Price: $12.00
   Sales tax: $ 0.60

_____

4. Item: book
   Price: $14.00
   Sales tax: $ 0.98

_____

5. Item: slides
   Price: $7.50
   Sales tax: $0.45

_____

6. Item: Chinese kite
   Price: $24.99
   Sales tax: $ 1.00

_____

7. Item: CD
   Price: $15.98
   Sales tax: $ 0.88

_____

8. Item: car stereo
   Price: $90.00
   Sales tax: $ 6.75

_____

Application

9. Carolyn ordered a traditional kimono from a Japanese import-export company in another state. The kimono price was $125. Sales tax was $8.75. Find the sales tax rate in the other state. _____

 10. Sometimes the quotient of the sales tax and the price does not work out evenly on your calculator. When this happens, round the quotient to the nearest thousandth before writing the percent. Suppose the price of a paperback book is $12.95 and the sales tax on the receipt is $0.66. What is the sales tax rate?

a. Divide 0.66 by 12.95. Write the number that appears on the screen.

_____

b. Round to the nearest thousandth.

_____

c. Write the state sales tax rate to the nearest tenth of a percent.

_____

INCOME TAX

Vocabulary

income tax: a tax based on the amount of money a person earns that is considered taxable by state and federal governments

In the United States, workers pay **income tax** on the money they earn. Each year, workers file federal income tax forms with the Internal Revenue Service. These forms tell the government how much workers earned that year, how much was taken from their paychecks to pay for taxes, and how much more tax they have to pay.

If line 37 (taxable income) is—		And you are—			
At least	But less than	Single	Married filing jointly	Married filing sepa-rately	Head of a house-hold
			Your tax is—		
3,400	3,450	124	03	197	124
3,450	3,500	130	08	203	129
3,500	3,550	138	14	209	135
3,550	3,600	142	19	215	140
3,600	3,650	148	25	221	146
3,650	3,700	154	30	227	151
3,700	3,750	160	36	233	157
3,750	3,800	166	41	239	162
3,800	3,850	172	47	245	168
3,850	3,900	178	52	252	173
3,900	3,950	184	58	259	179
3,950	4,000	190	63	266	184

Tax tables help you figure out how much to pay.

Hanan's taxable income last year was $3,942. Because this is between $3,900 and $3,950 and she is single, her tax is $184.

To find the tax rate she is paying, Hanan used this formula.

Tax rate = Tax ÷ Taxable income

$$r = \$184 \div \$3,942$$
$$r = 0.0466768$$
$$r = 4.66768\%$$

Rounded to the nearest whole percent, Hanan's tax rate is about 5%.

Guided Practice

1. Peter's taxable income is $3,500. He is the head of a household.

   a. Use the tax table to find his tax. _$135_

   b. Find his approximate tax rate. Use a calculator. Round to the nearest whole percent.

   $r = \$$ _____ $\div \$$ _____

   $r = $ _____ $= $ _____

Exercises

 Use the partial income tax table below to solve each problem. Use a calculator to help you. Round tax rates to the nearest whole percent.

2. Susan has a taxable income of $26,000. She is single.

   a. How much tax does she owe? _____

   b. What is her tax rate? _____

If line 37 (taxable income) is—		And you are—			
At least	But less than	Single	Married filing jointly	Married filing separately	Head of a household
			Your tax is—		
26,000					
26,000	26,050	4,873	3,821	6,074	4,513
26,050	26,100	4,888	3,834	6,093	4,527
26,100	26,150	4,903	3,846	6,112	4,541
26,150	26,200	4,918	3,859	6,131	4,555
35,000					
35,000	35,050	7,859	6,225	9,695	7,310
35,050	35,100	7,878	6,239	9,716	7,327
35,100	35,150	7,897	6,253	9,737	7,345
35,150	35,200	7,916	6,267	9,758	7,362

3. Luis has a taxable income of $35,100. He is married and files separately.

   a. How much tax does he owe? _____

   b. What is his tax rate? _____

Application

COOPERATIVE LEARNING

Work in small groups. Use the income tax table above to figure the following tax rates.

	Taxable Income	Single	Married Filing Jointly	Married Filing Separately	Head of Household
4.	$26,048				
5.	$35,010				

6. Share your results with others and describe any patterns you see.

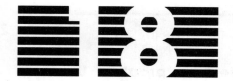

THE CALCULATOR PERCENT KEY

Vocabulary

percent key: key on a calculator identified by the "%" symbol; it changes a percent to a decimal

Reminder

Different calculators work in different ways, so consult your owner's manual or your teacher for directions.

Reminder

With many calculators, you may not need to press the [=] key to complete the calculation.

Using a calculator can help you solve percent problems quickly. Using the **percent key** on a calculator can help you work even more quickly.

You can use the percent key to find the percent of a number. For example, what is 75% of 24?

PRESS KEYS	DISPLAY READS
24 [X] 75 [%]	18

Example 1

How much will you pay for a $50 jacket if the sales tax rate is 6.5%? To solve this problem, add 6.5% of $50 to $50.

PRESS KEYS	DISPLAY READS
50 [+] 6.5 [%]	53.25

You will pay $53.25 for the jacket.

Example 2

Suppose you want to buy a CD of your favorite group on sale. Original price is $22. The discount rate is 15%. What is the sale price? To solve this problem, subtract 15% of $22 from $22.

PRESS KEYS	DISPLAY READS
22 [–] 15 [%]	18.7

The sale price of the CD is $18.70.

Guided Practice

1. Find 5% of $46.20.

   a. Write the sequence of digits and symbols you would enter.
   46.2 _[x]_ 5 _[%]_

   b. What does the display read? _____

   c. 5% of $46.20 = _____

Exercises

Use the percent key to solve. Round money amounts to the nearest cent.

2. 30% of 110 _____

3. 15% of 55 _____

4. 12% of $87.50 _____

5. 24% of $65.25 _____

6. 16% of $46.75 _____

7. 40% of $75.65 _____

8. 50% of $88.46 _____

9. 78% of $90.50 _____

10. 5.5% of $636.78 _____

11. 10.5% of $76.33 _____

Application

12. How much will you pay for an $85 set of free weights if the sales tax rate is 4.5%?

_____

13. Marcia wants to buy a book bag that is on sale. The list price is $38.45. The discount rate is 18%. What is the sale price of the book bag?

_____

14. Write answers to each question.

a. To solve Application 13 *without* a calculator, what steps would you take?

_____

_____

b. To solve Application 13 *using a calculator percent key*, what steps would you take?

_____

c. Which method is faster? _____

# FINDING THE BASE, EQUATION METHOD

Evan works in the school office during first period. Today, because of a flu outbreak, 150 students are absent. A vice principal asks Evan to record 150 absentees in the attendance book, then to record that 20% of the students are absent. How does the vice principal know that 20% are absent?

Evan reasons that the vice principal must know the total number of students in the school in order to calculate the percent absent. Evan uses this formula to find the total.

$$\text{Rate} \times \text{Base} = \text{Amount}$$

20% of what number is 150?

Reminder

The percent is the rate. "What number" is the base, b, and represents the total number of students.

$$0.20 \times b = 150 \quad \text{Write an equation.}$$

$$0.2b = 150 \quad \text{Multiply.}$$

$$\frac{0.2b}{0.2} = \frac{150}{0.2} \quad \text{Divide both sides by 0.2.}$$

$$b = 750$$

There are 750 students in Evan's school.

You can check the answer by finding 20% of 750.

Does $0.20 \times 750 = 150$?

Yes, the answer is correct.

Guided Practice

1. The next day, 60% of the absent students are boys. There are 72 boys absent. How many students in all are absent?

   a. Restate the problem.   60% of <u>what number</u> is <u>72</u> ?

   b. Write an equation. $0.60 \times$ _____ = _____

   c. Solve the equation. $b =$ _____

2. On Friday, eight teachers were absent from school. This is 25% of all the teachers. How many teachers are there in all?

a. Restate the problem. _____

b. Write an equation. _____

c. Solve the equation. _____

Exercises

Find the number.

3. 50% of what number is 7? _____

4. 20% of what number is 5? _____

5. 2% of what number is 8? _____

6. 60% of what number is 12? _____

7. 25% of what number is 5? _____

8. 80% of what number is 48? _____

Application

9. A school parent-teacher organization donated $400 to the school for field trips. This was 40% of the total amount the organization donated to the school. How much did the organization donate to the school?

_____

10. Draw a circle and cut it out. Shade about 25% of the circle.

a. If the *entire circle* represents 120, what number does the shaded portion represent? _____

b. If the *shaded portion* represents 120, what number does the whole circle represent? _____

 # FINDING THE BASE, PROPORTION METHOD

ABC MOTORS
ANNOUNCES
$1,200 OFF!
10% SAVINGS!
ALL 1995 MODELS

Armando wants to buy a car. His sister Alma shows him the ABC Motors advertisement. "I like saving 10%, or $1,200!" exclaims Armando. "But how much did the cars cost originally?"

To figure out the original price, Armando uses the proportion method.

10% of what number is $1,200?

$$\frac{10}{100} = \frac{1,200}{b}$$ Write a proportion.

$$10 \times b = 1,200 \times 100$$ Cross multiply.

$$10b = 120,000$$ Divide both sides by 10.

$$b = 12,000$$

The original price of the cars was $12,000.

Reminder

Write a proportion that is in the form $\frac{Rate}{100} = \frac{Amount}{Base}$.

Guided Practice

1. Yolanda has saved $600. This is 40% of the amount she needs for a down payment on a car. How much is her down payment?

   a. Restate the problem.

   <u>40%</u> of what number is   <u> $600 </u>

   b. Write a proportion.   _____

   c. Solve the proportion.   _____

2. Eric pays $200 each quarter to All-Good Insurance Co. for auto insurance. This is 25% of his total

yearly auto insurance premium. How much is his yearly auto insurance premium?

a. Restate the problem. _____

b. Write a proportion. _____

c. Solve the proportion. _____

Exercises

Find the number. Use the proportion method.

3. 20% of what number is 5?

_____

4. 6% of what number is 15?

_____

5. 30% of what number is 12?

_____

6. 80% of what number is 16?

_____

7. 75% of what number is 24?

_____

8. 90% of what number is 126?

_____

Application

9. Yolanda finally saved $1,500, the full amount of the down payment on a new car. The down payment was 20% of the price of the car. What was the price of the car she wanted to buy? _____

10. Draw a circle and cut it out. Shade about 40% of the circle.

a. If the shaded portion represents 160, what number does the unshaded portion represent? _____

b. Shade about 60% of the circle. If the shaded portion represents 240, what number does the unshaded portion represent?

_____

c. Explain your results.

_____

_____

_____

 # COMPOUND INTEREST

Vocabulary

compound interest: the interest calculated on a principal that includes previous interest earned

When you deposit money in a bank, you may earn either simple or compound interest. If you earn simple interest, you earn a percentage of the original deposit.

For example, if you deposit $100 into an account earning 7% simple interest each year, you would receive 7% of $100, or $7.00, each year that you leave the money in the account. In two years, you would have $114 in the account.

When you earn **compound interest**, you earn interest on your interest. At the end of each time period, your interest is added to the amount in the account. You then earn interest on the total amount in the next time period.

For example, if you deposit $100 into an account earning 7% compound interest each year, you would receive $7.00 in interest the first year. Your balance would be $107. The second year, you would receive 7% interest on the *new balance* of $107, or $7.49. So after two years, this account would have a balance of $114.49.

You can compare the five-year growth of a savings account earning simple interest and compound interest.

Example 1

Suppose you deposit $1,000 in a savings account that earns 7% simple interest yearly. How much money will be in the account after five years?

Reminder

The principal is the amount of money borrowed or saved.

	Simple Interest		
Period	Principal	Interest	Total
1	$1,000	$1,000 × 0.07 = $70	$1,070
2	$1,000	$1,000 × 0.07 = $70	$1,140
3	$1,000	$1,000 × 0.07 = $70	$1,210
4	$1,000	$1,000 × 0.07 = $70	$1,280
5	$1,000	$1,000 × 0.07 = $70	$1,350

There will be $1,350 in the account after five years. Note that the principal does not change, even though the total amount in the account grows with interest.

Example 2

Suppose you deposit $1,000 in a savings account that earns 7% interest compounded yearly. How much money will be in the account after five years?

Compound Interest			
Period	Principal	Interest	Total
1	$1,000	$1,000 × 0.07 = $70	$1,070
2	$1,070	$1,070 × 0.07 = $74.90	$1,144.90
3	$1,144.90	$1,144.90 × 0.07 = $80.14	$1,225.04
4	$1,225.04	$1,225.04 × 0.07 = $85.75	$1,310.79
5	$1,310.79	$1,310.79 × 0.07 = $91.76	$1,402.55

There will be $1,402.55 in the account after five years. Note that each year, the principal is equal to the previous year's total.

In the same amount of time, five years, your $1,000 deposit earned $52.55 more in an account in which interest is compounded yearly than in an account earning simple interest.

To compute compound interest more quickly, use your calculator and this formula:

Reminder

Rate, r, is the percent.

Total amount = principal + (rate × principal)

$$A = p + (r \times p)$$

Look back at the compound interest table. Use the calculator percent key to find the first and second years' totals.

Reminder

On some calculators, you do not have to press the ▣ key to complete the computation.

PRESS KEYS: DISPLAY READS:

🔢 1 0 0 0 ➕ 7 %   7 0

＝   1 0 7 0

➕ 7 %   7 4 . 9

＝   1 1 4 4 . 9 0

The calculator percent key saves you work.

1. Carlita deposits $300 in a savings account that pays 5% interest compounded yearly. She plans to leave the money in the account for two years. How much will be in the account after two years?

   a. How much interest is earned in the first year?

   $300 × 0.05 = _____*$15*_____

   b. What is the principal after the first year?

   $300 + $15 = _____

   c. How much interest is earned in the second year?

   Interest: _____ × 0.05 = _____

   d. What is the principal after the second year? _____

2. Two years ago, Mr. Jung bought a certificate of deposit (CD) for $2,000. The CD paid 6% interest compounded yearly. How much is the CD worth today?

   a. How much interest was earned in the first year?

   $2,000 × _____ = _____

   b. What was the principal after the first year? _____

   c. How much interest was earned in the second year?

   _____ × _____ = _____

   d. How much is the CD worth after two years? _____

Exercises

 Find the total interest each account earns if interest is compounded yearly.

3. Principal: $100

   Rate: 5%

   Time: 2 years

   _____

4. Principal: $200

   Rate: 6%

   Time: 2 years

   _____

5. Principal: $3,000

   Rate: 4%

   Time: 3 years

   _____

6. Principal: $2,500

   Rate: 7%

   Time: 4 years

   _____

Find the total amount in each account if interest is compounded yearly.

7. Principal: $500

    Rate: 3%

    Time: 2 years

    _____

8. Principal: $800

    Rate: 8%

    Time: 3 years

    _____

9. Principal: $1,200

    Rate: 6%

    Time: 4 years

    _____

10. Principal: $3,525

    Rate: 5.5%

    Time: 5 years

    _____

Application

 11. Frank wants to buy a car. He takes out a four-year bank loan for $4,500 at 12% interest compounded yearly. How much interest does he pay in all on the loan?

_____

12. When Liu was 12 years old, her family deposited $1,500 in an account for her college education. The account pays 5% interest compounded yearly. How much is the account worth now that she is 17 years old?

_____

13. Explain the difference between simple interest and interest compounded yearly.

 _____

_____

_____

 # MIXED APPLICATIONS OF PERCENT

Reminder

Amount = Rate × Base

There are three types of percent problems.

Type 1: 25% of 12 is what number?

Type 2: What percent of 12 is 3?

Type 3: 25% of what number is 3?

You can solve percent problems by writing an equation or by writing a proportion.

Example 1

20% of 25 is what number?

Equation Method	**Proportion Method**

$$20\% \text{ of } 25 = n$$
$$n = 0.2 \times 25$$
$$n = 5$$

$$20\% \text{ of } 25 = n$$
$$\frac{20}{100} = \frac{n}{25}$$
$$100n = 500$$
$$n = 5$$

So, 20% of 25 is 5.   So, 20% of 25 is 5.

Check your answer.   Check your answer.

$$\text{Does } 0.2 \times 25 = 5?$$ $$\text{Does } \frac{20}{100} = \frac{5}{25}?$$
$$\text{Yes, } 5 = 5.$$ $$\text{Does } 20 \times 25 = 100 \times 5?$$
$$\text{Yes, } 500 = 500.$$

The answer is correct.   The answer is correct.

You can also solve real-world problems involving percents.

Example 2

Julius typed 9 pages of a 12-page term paper. What percent of the term paper has he typed?

What percent of 12 is 9?   Restate the problem.

$r \times 12 = 9$ Write an equation.

$\dfrac{12r}{12} = \dfrac{9}{12}$ Solve.

$r = \dfrac{9}{12} = 0.75$

Julius has typed 75% of his term paper.

Sometimes you only need an estimate to solve a problem.

Example 3

30% of what number is 90?

Write a proportion: $\dfrac{30}{100} = \dfrac{90}{b}$

Cross multiply: $30 \times b = 90 \times 100$

Divide both sides by 30: $30b = 9000$

$b = 300$

Example 4

Roger and Enya are dining at the Red Dragon Thai Restaurant. The bill for their dinner totals $29.78 without tax. They want to leave a tip of 15% of the cost of the meal. About how much should Roger and Enya leave as a tip?

Think: *$29.78 is about $30 and 15% = 10% + 5%.*

Estimate:

1. You know that 10% of $30 is $3.

2. Since 5% is half of 10%, then 5% of $30 is half of $3, or $1.50.

3. Then 15% of $30 is about $3 + $1.50, or $4.50.

Roger and Enya should leave $4.50 as a tip.

You can use compatible numbers to make estimates.

Example 5

Estimate 48% of $60.

48% is close to 50%, or $\dfrac{1}{2}$.   Think.

$\dfrac{1}{2} \times 60 = 30$ Solve.

So, 48% of $60 is about $30.

Reminder

Compatible numbers are numbers that are easy to work with mentally.

Reminder

$\dfrac{1}{3} = 33\dfrac{1}{3}\%$ $\dfrac{1}{10} = 10\%$

$\dfrac{1}{4} = 25\%$ $\dfrac{2}{3} = 66\dfrac{2}{3}\%$

$\dfrac{1}{5} = 20\%$ $\dfrac{3}{4} = 75\%$

Guided Practice

Write the equation and the proportion that you could use to solve each percent problem.

1. 2% of 24 is what number?

   a. Equation: $0.02 \times \underline{24} = n$

   b. Proportion: $\underline{\frac{2}{100} = \frac{n}{24}}$

2. 15% of what number is 16?

   a. Equation: _____

   b. Proportion: _____

3. About 70% of a person's body weight is water. For a person who weighs 150 pounds, how much of the weight is water?

   a. Restate the problem.   70% of _____ is w

   b. Write an equation. $0.7 \times$ _____ $= w$

   c. Solve.   _____ $= w$

Exercises

Choose the most reasonable estimate. Write *a*, *b*, or *c*.

4. 40% of $28.98 _____

   a. $\frac{2}{5}$ of $30

   b. $\frac{2}{5}$ of $25

   c. $\frac{2}{5}$ of $20

5. 26% of $100 _____

   a. $\frac{3}{10}$ of $100

   b. $\frac{1}{5}$ of $100

   c. $\frac{1}{4}$ of $100

6. 30% of $31.09 _____

   a. $10

   b. $9

   c. $8

7. 21% of $50 _____

   a. $12.50

   b. $11

   c. $10

 Solve. Use the equation method or the proportion method. Check your answers.

8. 90% of what number is 18?

_____

9. What percent of 55 is 11?

_____

10. 18% of 150 is what number?

_____

11. 75% of what number is 60?

_____

12. Of the 800 students at Central High School, 20 students did not vote for any of the candidates for student council president. What percent of the students did not vote?

_____

13. Suppose you see a Food-O-Matic advertised on TV for 20% off the regular price of $19.95. About how much is the sale price?

_____

14. The circle graph below shows the results of surveying 60 students about their leisure-time activities.

Leisure-Time Activities

a. About what percent preferred dancing? _____

b. About how many students is this? _____

c. About what percent preferred watching TV? _____

d. About how many students is this? _____

15. Kevin eats lunch at an Italian café. The bill totals $7.99 without tax. He wants to leave a tip of 15% of the cost of the meal. Describe how to estimate the amount of the tip.

_____

_____

_____

1-3 CUMULATIVE REVIEW

Complete.

1. What percent of the figure is shaded?

_____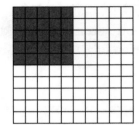

2. Shade 25% of the figure.

Write each decimal as a percent.

3. 0.34 = _____   **4.** 0.27 = _____   **5.** 0.205 = _____

Write each percent as a decimal.

6. 82% = _____   **7.** 7% = _____   **8.** 40% = _____

Write each fraction as a percent.

9. $\frac{1}{4}$ = _____   **10.** $\frac{2}{3}$ = _____   **11.** $\frac{1}{8}$ = _____

Write each percent as a fraction in simplest form.

12. 90% = _____   **13.** 35% = _____   **14.** 12% = _____

Use mental math to change each fraction to a percent.

15. $\frac{1}{2}$ = _____   **16.** $\frac{3}{5}$ = _____   **17.** $\frac{9}{10}$ = _____

Answer the question below.

18. Look at the following words and think about what they mean: *century, cent, centipede, centimeter*. What do these words have in common with the word *percent*? How does this help you remember what percent means?

 _____

_____

4-7 CUMULATIVE REVIEW

Complete.

1. What percent of the figure at the right is shaded? _____

Write each mixed number as a percent.

2. $1\frac{1}{4} =$ _____   3. $3\frac{3}{10} =$ _____   4. $2\frac{1}{8} =$ _____

Write each percent as a mixed number in simplest form.

5. $250\% =$ _____   6. $475\% =$ _____   7. $120\% =$ _____

Complete.

Fraction	Decimal	Percent
8.	0.45	9.
$\frac{3}{5}$	10.	11.
12.	13.	90%

Use the equation or proportion method to find the percent of the number.

14. What is 20% of 250?

_____

15. What is 92% of 880?

_____

16. Shade 75% of the dots at the right.

17. Wei-Chi answered 87.5% of the problems on her test correctly. There were a total of 80 problems on the test. How many problems did she answer correctly?

_____

8-12 CUMULATIVE REVIEW

 Find the sale price for each item.

1. In-line skates for $200; 15% discount

2. Stereo system for $755; 25% discount

_____

_____

Find the total purchase price for each item.

3. Fifi jeans: $50; 7% tax

4. Running shoes: $78.80; 5% tax

_____

_____

Solve each problem.

5. Enrique borrowed $500 from a bank to buy a stereo. How much interest would he pay for 2 years if the simple interest rate was 8%?

_____

6. Yolanda deposited $860 into a savings account that earned 4.5% simple interest. How much money would she have in the account after 6 months? (Hint: Add the interest to the principal.)

_____

Complete the table. Write the mixed number in simplest form.

Fraction	Decimal	Percent
7.	0.005	8.
$\frac{1}{500}$	9.	10.
11.	12.	0.25%

Estimate each answer.

13. 32% of 146 _____

14. 76% of 201 _____

15. $10\frac{1}{2}$% of 62 _____

16. 3.5% of 31 _____

13-16 CUMULATIVE REVIEW

Write and solve an equation to find the rate.

1. What percent of 8 is 2?

2. What percent of 60 is 21?

_____

_____

Write and solve a proportion to find the rate.

3. What percent of 14 is 7?

4. What percent of 75 is 21?

_____

_____

Find the discount rate for each item.

5. Item: boots
List price: $125
Sale price: $105

6. Item: watch
List price: $50
Sale price: $30

7. Item: video game
List price: $24
Sale price: $21

_____

_____

_____

Find the sales tax rate for each item.

8. Item: court shoes
Price: $48.00
Sales tax: $ 2.40

9. Item: T-shirt
Price: $16.00
Sales tax: $ 0.96

10. Item: purse
Price: $24.99
Sales tax: $ 0.75

_____

_____

_____

Solve each problem.

11. Amy bought a paint set for $19.99. The original price was $29.99. What were the discount and the discount rate? _____

12. Chris got 45 out of 50 math test questions correct. What percent of the questions did he answer correctly? _____

13. An exercise machine is on sale for $80. The list price is $119.99. Find the discount and the discount rate. _____

14. While visiting her grandmother, Shanice bought a painting of the Everglades for $45. The sales tax was $2.70. Find the sales tax rate in Shanice's grandmother's state. _____

Use this partial income tax table to answer Exercises 1 and 2. Round tax rates to the nearest whole percent.

If line 37 (taxable income) is—		And you are—			
At least	But less than	Single	Married filing jointly	Married filing separately	Head of a household
		Your tax is—			
5,000	5,050	329	179	413	306
5,050	5,100	336	184	420	312
5,100	5,150	343	190	427	318
5,150	5,200	350	195	434	324

1. Juan has a taxable income of $5,075. He is single.

   a. How much tax does he owe? _____

   b. What is his tax rate? _____

2. Inga has a taxable income of $5,190. She is married and filing separately.

   a. How much tax does she owe? _____

   b. What is her approximate tax rate? _____

 Use the percent key to solve each percent problem.

3. 18% of $35.00 _____   4. 70% of $98.50 _____

Find the number. Use the equation method.

5. 25% of what number is 10?   6. 75% of what number is 72?

   _____   _____

Find the number. Use the proportion method.

7. 5% of what number is 10?   8. 45% of what number is 54?

   _____   _____

Solve each problem.

9. How much will you pay for a $150 keyboard if the sales tax rate is 5.5%?

   _____

10. George has saved $500. This is 40% of what he needs for a down payment on a car. How much is the down payment?

   _____

Find the total interest each account earns, if interest is compounded yearly.

1. Principal: $100
   Rate: 4%
   Time: 2 years

   _____

2. Principal: $250
   Rate: 5%
   Time: 2 years

   _____

3. Principal: $1,500
   Rate: 6%
   Time: 3 years

   _____

4. Principal: $4,500
   Rate: 7%
   Time: 4 years

   _____

Find the total amount in each account, if interest is compounded yearly.

5. Principal: $100
   Rate: 3%
   Time: 2 years

   _____

6. Principal: $1,200
   Rate: 6%
   Time: 5 years

   _____

Solve. Use the equation method or the proportion method. Check your answers.

7. 85% of what number is 68?

   _____

8. What percent of 95 is 23?

   _____

9. Nell borrows $2,800 for 3 years at 9% interest compounded yearly to pay for a motorcycle. How much interest does she pay on the loan?

   _____

10. Stanley eats dinner at a French restaurant. The bill totals $31.78 without tax. He wants to leave a tip of 15% of the cost of the meal. About how much does he leave for a tip? Use mental math skills to estimate the tip.

   _____

ANSWER KEY

LESSON 1 (pp. 2–3)

   1. a. 100   **b.** 43   **c.** 43%

   3. 50%   **5.** 5%   **7.** 83 of the 100 parts shaded

   9. 50 pennies

   11. Sample: Only 36% of the runners completed the race due to unseasonably hot weather.

LESSON 2 (pp. 4–5)

   1. a. 37   **b.** 37%

   3. 20%   **5.** 15.5%   **7.** 55%   **9.** 0.50   **11.** 0.97

   13. 0.01   **15.** 0.15; 15%   **17.** 0.90; 90%

LESSON 3 (pp. 6–7)

   1. a. 0.75   **b.** 75%   **3.** 20%   **5.** 37.5%

   7. $\frac{1}{25}$ **9.** 50%; 32%; 40%; 60%; 80%; 5%

LESSON 4 (pp. 8–9)

   1. a. $\frac{6}{5}$ **b.** 1.2   **c.** 120%   **3.** 175%   **5.** 225%

   7. 330%   **9.** $1\frac{3}{4}$ **11.** $2\frac{1}{4}$ **13.** $3\frac{3}{4}$

   15. Sample: Shanti and Deb got more orders than they had estimated: 125% of 4 is 5, one more order than they had planned on.

LESSON 5 (pp. 10–13)

   1. a. 40.   **b.** 0.4   **c.** 0.4

   3. a. 37.5   **b.** 37.5%

   5. $\frac{1}{5}$ **7.** 20%   **9.** e   **11.** b   **13.** a

   15. d   **17.** 10%   **19.** 25%   **21.** 0.4   **23.** 75%

   25. $83\frac{1}{3}$%   **27.** 0.5   **29.** 80%   **31.** 1.0

LESSON 6 (pp. 14–15)

   1. a. 240   **b.** 65%   **c.** 240   **d.** 0.65; $\frac{65}{100}$

   e. $a = 0.65 \times 240$; $a = 156$ students

   3. $a = 0.1 \times 300$ or $a = \frac{1}{10} \times 300$; $a = 30$

   5. $a = 1 \times 153$; $a = 153$

   7. $a = 0.08 \times 125$; $a = 10$

   9. $a = 0.15 \times 320$; $a = 48$

   11. 20   **13.** 28   **15.** 4

   17. Sample: Percents that are factors of 100 are easy to work with mentally, and these conversions can be done more quickly without a calculator.

LESSON 7 (pp. 16–17)

   1. a. $\frac{20}{100} = \frac{n}{15}$ **b.** $100n = 300$

   c. $n = \frac{300}{100}$ **d.** $n = 3$

   3. 294.5   **5.** 21   **7.** 341   **9.** 47.52

LESSON 8 (pp. 18–19)

   1. a. 0.25   **b.** $120   **c.** $0.25 \times \$120 = \$30$

   d. $\$120 - \$30 = \$90$

   3. $9.50   **5.** $22.43   **7.** $17.49

   9. $\$115 \times 70\% = \$80.50$

LESSON 9 (pp. 20–21)

   1. a. 0.05   **b.** $65.90

   c. $\$65.90 \times 0.05 = \$3.295$ or $3.30

   d. $\$65.90 + 3.30 = \$69.20$

   3. $6.54; $137.34   **5.** $70.40; $1,350.40

   7. $0.85; $19.75

   9. Mario noticed that when you add the tax to the purchase price (100% + 5%) you get 105%. This is the purchase price plus tax, or $81.90.

LESSON 10 (pp. 22–23)

   1. a. $I = p \times r \times t$

   b. $\$750 \times 0.035 \times 3$ **c.** $78.75

   3. $27   **5.** $63.00

LESSON 11 (pp. 24–25)

   1. a. 20%   **b.** $\frac{1}{5}$ **c.** 140   **d.** $140 \div 5 = 28$

   3. 200   **5.** 10   **7.** 270   **9.** 100   **11.** about $8

LESSON 12 (pp. 26–27)

   1. a. 0.3   **b.** 0.003   **3.** 0.008

   5. 0.7%   **7.** 0.125%   **9.** 0.00875

LESSON 13 (pp. 28–29)

   1. a. 24   **b.** 48; 48; 24; 48; 0.5   **c.** 50%

   3. $r \times 12 = 9$; 75%   **5.** $r \times 120 = 15$; about 13%

   7. 31%   **9.** 93%

LESSON 14 (pp. 30–31)

   1. a. $\frac{r}{100} = \frac{12}{20}$ **b.** 60   **c.** 60%

   3. 80%   **5.** 60%   **7.** 71%   **9.** 67%   **11.** 75%

LESSON 15 (pp. 32–33)

  1. a. $9; $3 **b.** $3; 0.25; 25

  3. discount = $15; discount rate = 50%

  5. discount = $15; discount rate = 13%

  7. discount = $10; discount rate = 17%

  9. 20%; 40%

LESSON 16 (pp. 34–35)

  1. a. $0.60 **b.** 0.06 **c.** 6%

  3. 5% **5.** 6% **7.** 5.5% **9.** 7%

LESSON 17 (pp. 36–37)

  1. a. $135 **b.** 0.0385714; about 4%

  3. a. $9,737 **b.** about 28%

  5. $35,000; 22%; 18%; 28%; 21%

LESSON 18 (pp. 38–39)

  1. a. 46.20 [×] 5 [%]

  b. 2.3100000 **c.** $2.31

  3. 8.25 **5.** $15.66 **7.** $30.26

  9. $70.59 **11.** $8.01 **13.** $31.53

LESSON 19 (pp. 40–41)

  1. a. what number; 72 **b.** $0.6b = 72$

  c. $b = 120$ **3.** 14

  5. 400 **7.** 20 **9.** $1,000

LESSON 20 (pp. 42–43)

  1. a. 40%; $600 **b.** $\frac{40}{100} = \frac{600}{n}$ **c.** $n = \$1,500$

  3. 25 **5.** 40 **7.** 32 **9.** $7,500

LESSON 21 (pp. 44–47)

  1. a. $15 **b.** $315 **c.** $315; $15.75

  d. $330.75

  3. $10.25 **5.** $374.59 **7.** $530.45

  9. $1,514.97 **11.** $2,580.84

  13. Simple interest is a percent of the original deposit each time period; compound interest is interest earned on both the original deposit and on all the interest earned before the current time period.

LESSON 22 (pp. 48–51)

  1. a. 24 **b.** $\frac{n}{24}$

  3. a. 150 lb

  b. 150 **c.** 105 lb

  5. c **7.** c **9.** 20% **11.** 80 **13.** about $16

  15. Estimate that $7.99 is about $8.00. Estimate that 10% of $8 is $.80, and that 5% of $8 is $\frac{1}{2}$ of $.80, or $.40. So $.80 + $.40 = a tip of $1.20.

CUMULATIVE REVIEW (L1–L3) (p. 52)

1. 25%   **3.** 34%   **5.** 20.5%   **7.** 0.07   **9.** 25%

11. 12.5% or $12\frac{1}{2}$%   **13.** $\frac{7}{20}$ **15.** 50%

17. 90%

CUMULATIVE REVIEW (L4–L7) (p. 53)

1. 125%   **3.** 330%   **5.** $2\frac{1}{2}$ **7.** $1\frac{1}{5}$ **9.** 45%

11. 60%   **13.** 0.9   **15.** 809.6   **17.** 70

CUMULATIVE REVIEW (L8–L12) (p. 54)

1. $170   **3.** $53.50   **5.** $80   **7.** $\frac{1}{200}$ **9.** 0.002

11. $\frac{1}{400}$ **13.** 45   **15.** 6

CUMULATIVE REVIEW (L13–L16) (p. 55)

1. $n \times 8 = 2$; 25%   **3.** 50%   **5.** 16%

7. 12.5%   **9.** 6%   **11.** $10; $33\frac{1}{3}$%

13. $39.99; $33\frac{1}{3}$%

CUMULATIVE REVIEW (L17–L20) (p. 56)

1. a. $336   **b.** 7%

3. $6.30   **5.** 40   **7.** 200   **9.** $158.25

CUMULATIVE REVIEW (L21–L22) (p. 57)

1. $8.16   **3.** $286.52   **5.** $106.09   **7.** 80

9. $826.08